SKYSCRAPERS

SKYSCRAPERS
was created by
McRae Publishing Ltd, London
www.mcraepublishing.co.uk

Publishers: Anne McRae, Marco Nardi

Author: Chris Oxlade
Consultant: Martha Thorne
Main Illustrations: Leonello Calvetti pp. 16-17, 24-25, 26-27, 28-29, 40-41;
Manuela Cappon pp. 20-21; Lorenzo Cecchi pp. 10, 13, 14-15, 22-23, 30-31, 38-39;
Studio Stalio (Alessandro Cantucci, Fabiano Fabbrucci, Margherita Salvadori,
Ivan Stalio) pp. 9, 18-19, 32, 33, 34, 37, 42, 43, 44
Other Illustrations: Lucia Mattioli, Studio Stalio
Maps: Paola Baldanzi
Graphic Design: Marco Nardi
Layout: Rebecca Milner
Project Editor: Claire Moore
Repro: Litocolor, Florence
Art Director: Marco Nardi

An Imprint of Sterling Publishing
387 Park Avenue South
New York, NY 10016

ISBN 978-1-4351-5434-6

Manufactured in China
Lot #:
2 4 6 8 10 9 7 5 3 1
02/14

Chris Oxlade

SKYSCRAPERS

Sandy Creek
NEW YORK

Table of Contents

Introduction 7

Through Antiquity 8

The First Skyscrapers 10

The Eclectic Period 12

The Art Deco Period 14

The Chrysler Building 16

Unusual Shapes 18

Everyday Life of a Skyscraper 20

The International Style 22

The New York Skyline 24

The Supertall Period 26

Skyscrapers of the East 28

Recent Styles 30

The Hong Kong and Shanghai Bank 32

Coping with the Natural World 34

The World Trade Center 36

Into the 21st Century 38

The Petronas Towers 40

The World's Tallest 42

Future Plans 44

Index 46

Introduction

Standing high above the streets, often disappearing into the clouds, skyscrapers are one of humankind's greatest achievements. These towering buildings are proof of our skill at architecture and engineering, and hold thousands of tons of floors, machinery, and people hundreds of feet up in the sky. Resistant to hurricane-force winds and the most violent earthquakes, they are testimony to our understanding of science and technology.

Like self-contained towns, skyscrapers create a huge amount of valuable living and working space in busy cities around the world. Many of the tallest skyscrapers, however, are mostly for show and are symbols of commercial success. Fierce competition for the title of "world's tallest" has gone on for much of the history of the skyscraper.

Beginning in the 1880s in Chicago, skyscrapers were first made possible with the development of the steel frame and the invention of the elevator. Since then skyscrapers have been created with many different architectural styles, from medieval-style spires and Art Deco sculpture to vast walls of glass. The United States was once considered the "home" of the skyscraper, but they are now scattered across the skylines of cities all around the world. Taller and taller skyscrapers are being built in cities in Asia, the Middle East, and Europe. Despite the tragic events of September 11, 2001, architects and engineers still strive to build bigger, better, and more interesting buildings that reflect recent trends in architecture. Today's buildings are ten times taller than the first skyscrapers. The ambitions of countries, cities, and businesses, and the egos of entrepreneurs, will undoubtedly push them even higher during the course of the 21st century.

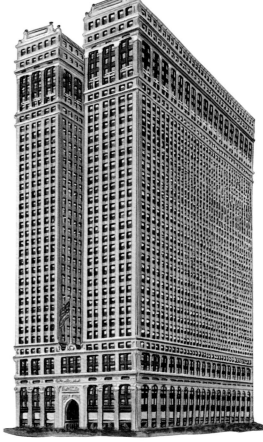

Through Antiquity

The first skyscrapers were built just over a hundred years ago, but tall buildings have existed for thousands of years. Most ancient tall buildings were religious monuments, such as the pyramids of Egypt, the temples of Central America, the pagodas of the Far East, and the medieval cathedrals of Europe. These huge buildings were all built from stone blocks or mud bricks, the only materials available for tall buildings until the 19th century.

The Tower of Babel in a painting by Pieter Bruegel the Elder from 1563.

Right: The spiral-shaped minaret of the Great Mosque at Samarra in Iraq was completed in 852 A.D. and is 170 feet (52 m) high.

The Tower of Babel

The Tower of Babel is described in the Bible as a "tower with its top in the heavens." But did it really exist? Archeologists think that the tower, thought to have been 300 feet (90 m) tall, was a ziggurat in the ancient city of Babylon, in modern-day Iraq. The city is now in ruins, but the foundations of a huge mud-brick structure still exist.

Islamic Minarets

The earliest minaret, the tower from which a muezzin calls Muslims to prayer, was built in Tunisia in the 8th century. Many minarets are finely decorated and soar high into the sky to a pencil-shaped point.

Fourteen of the original 72 defensive towers stand in San Gimignano.

The Palazzo Contarini del Bovolo, a 15th-century multi-story house in Venice, Italy.

Medieval Towers

Tall, narrow towers were more difficult to build from stone masonry than pyramids or ziggurats. Careful and accurate construction was needed. Most towers were church or cathedral bell towers, such as the Leaning Tower of Pisa, completed in 1271. Other towers were built for defense, such as those in the medieval town of San Gimignano in Italy (above).

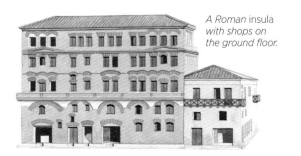

A Roman insula *with shops on the ground floor.*

High-Rise Homes

Finding space to live in a busy city is a problem that has existed for thousands of years. The ancient Romans built apartment blocks, known as *insulae*, up to six stories high in Rome. Made from wood and mud bricks, they sometimes collapsed or burned down.

Many tall churches were built during the medieval period. Burgos Cathedral (left) in Spain was completed in 1221 and its Gothic towers were added in the 15th century.

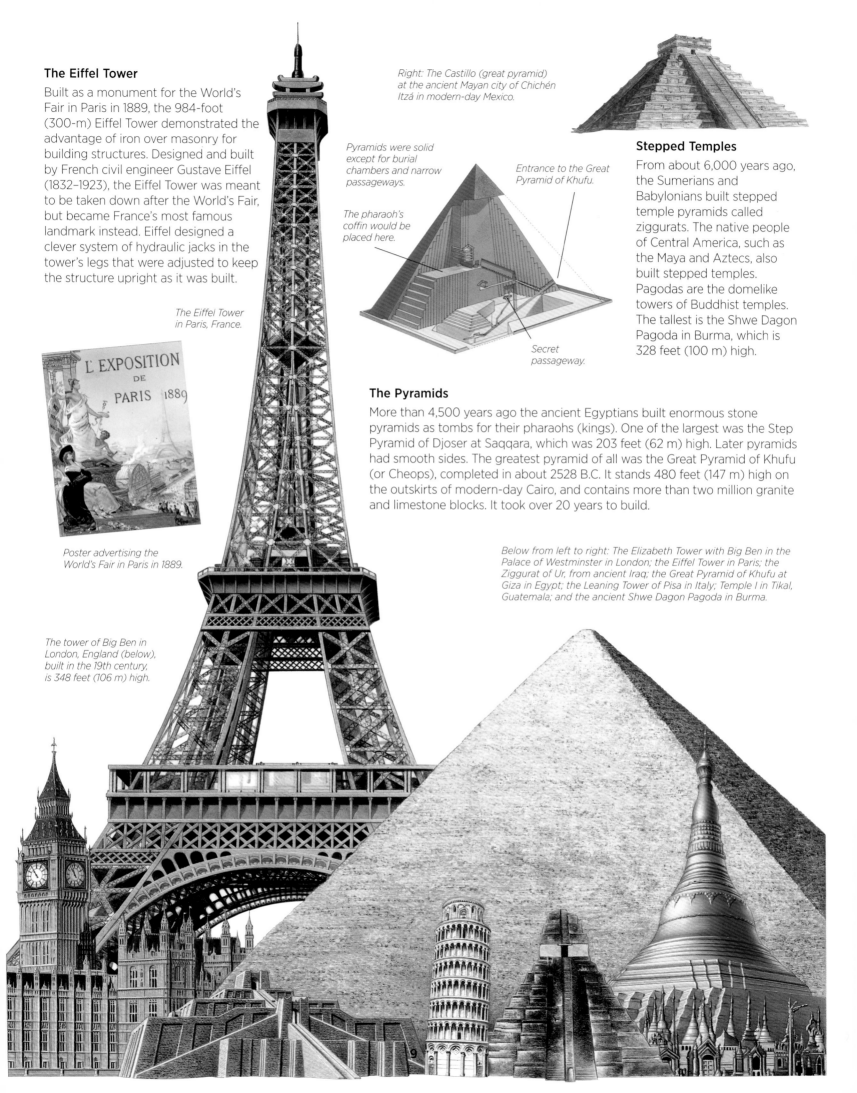

The Eiffel Tower

Built as a monument for the World's Fair in Paris in 1889, the 984-foot (300-m) Eiffel Tower demonstrated the advantage of iron over masonry for building structures. Designed and built by French civil engineer Gustave Eiffel (1832–1923), the Eiffel Tower was meant to be taken down after the World's Fair, but became France's most famous landmark instead. Eiffel designed a clever system of hydraulic jacks in the tower's legs that were adjusted to keep the structure upright as it was built.

The Eiffel Tower in Paris, France.

Poster advertising the World's Fair in Paris in 1889.

The tower of Big Ben in London, England (below), built in the 19th century, is 348 feet (106 m) high.

Right: The Castillo (great pyramid) at the ancient Mayan city of Chichén Itzá in modern-day Mexico.

Pyramids were solid except for burial chambers and narrow passageways.

The pharaoh's coffin would be placed here.

Entrance to the Great Pyramid of Khufu.

Secret passageway.

Stepped Temples

From about 6,000 years ago, the Sumerians and Babylonians built stepped temple pyramids called ziggurats. The native people of Central America, such as the Maya and Aztecs, also built stepped temples. Pagodas are the domelike towers of Buddhist temples. The tallest is the Shwe Dagon Pagoda in Burma, which is 328 feet (100 m) high.

The Pyramids

More than 4,500 years ago the ancient Egyptians built enormous stone pyramids as tombs for their pharaohs (kings). One of the largest was the Step Pyramid of Djoser at Saqqara, which was 203 feet (62 m) high. Later pyramids had smooth sides. The greatest pyramid of all was the Great Pyramid of Khufu (or Cheops), completed in about 2528 B.C. It stands 480 feet (147 m) high on the outskirts of modern-day Cairo, and contains more than two million granite and limestone blocks. It took over 20 years to build.

Below from left to right: The Elizabeth Tower with Big Ben in the Palace of Westminster in London; the Eiffel Tower in Paris; the Ziggurat of Ur, from ancient Iraq; the Great Pyramid of Khufu at Giza in Egypt; the Leaning Tower of Pisa in Italy; Temple I in Tikal, Guatemala; and the ancient Shwe Dagon Pagoda in Burma.

The New York Times building of 1888 was one of New York's earliest skyscrapers.

The top two floors of Chicago's Home Insurance Building (right) were added in 1891. It was demolished in 1931.

William Le Baron Jenney was a talented structural engineer and architect, and one of the founders of the Chicago school. He is known as the "father of the skyscraper."

The Home Insurance Building

Most skyscraper experts think of Chicago's Home Insurance Building, completed in 1885, as the first real skyscraper. It had just ten stories and was designed and built by William Le Baron Jenney (1832–1907). The two rear walls were masonry bearing-wall construction, while the two street façades used iron to reinforce the masonry and reduce its size. The slender frame allowed the building to have much larger windows than previous buildings, which were recessed to make the building look taller. The frame was covered in plaster to make it fireproof.

Early Skyscraper Frames

All skyscrapers have a steel or concrete frame. The frame supports the weight of the building and everything in it. In early skyscrapers, the frame was made up of vertical columns and horizontal beams. The beams carried weight from the floors to the columns, and the columns carried the weight down to strong foundations in the ground.

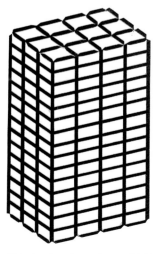

This drawing shows the semirigid steel frame of the Reliance Building, built in Chicago in 1895.

The First Skyscrapers

Up until the middle of the 19th century all tall buildings relied on sturdy masonry walls to hold them up. Near the bottom of the building the walls needed to be very thick and could only have tiny windows. Then civil engineers invented a completely new way of supporting a building. This was the metal frame, which made it possible to build a new type of building—the skyscraper. The first skyscrapers were built in the 1880s and 1890s in the city of Chicago.

Right: A detail from Louis Sullivan's Guaranty Building, built between 1894 and 1895.

Architect Louis Sullivan (1856–1924) said that every skyscraper should have its own identity.

The Chicago School

Many architects moved to Chicago during the building boom that took place after the catastrophic fire of 1871. Among them were William Le Baron Jenney, John Wellborn Root, Daniel Burnham, and Louis Sullivan. They designed many of the first skyscrapers, and became known as the Chicago school. Sullivan designed his skyscrapers to emphasize their function and height.

Over 1,000 people died in the Chicago fire and 340,000 were left homeless.

Fire in Chicago

By the middle of the 19th century Chicago was a busy commercial center and growing fast. One day in 1871 a fire broke out in the city center. It spread quickly through the city's wooden buildings and walkways (below), and more than a third of the city was destroyed. Rebuilding began immediately, and land prices in the city center skyrocketed. These economic constraints meant buildings grew taller, while the invention of the elevator and fireproofing also enabled buildings to become higher.

Reaching New Heights

Chicago's tallest skyscraper in the 19th century was the 22-story Masonic Temple, completed in 1892. It was designed by Daniel Burnham and John Wellborn Root, and at 302 feet (92 m) high was the world's tallest building for two years. Due to restrictions on tall buildings in Chicago, it was also the city's tallest building until the 1920s. Meanwhile, skyscrapers were springing up in New York, too. The city's first skyscraper was the six-story Equitable Building, completed in 1870.

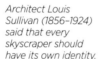

The Masonic Temple.

Elevators

Skyscrapers would be impractical without elevators for reaching the upper floors quickly and easily. A safety elevator (that did not fall if its support cable broke) was invented by Elisha Otis (1811–61) in the 1850s. His invention helped change peoples' feelings about using elevators in a high-rise building. The first passenger elevator was installed in a department store in New York in 1857.

Right: An early elevator in use in a tall building.

The Woolworth Building.

Frank Winfield Woolworth.

The Eclectic Period

The first period in skyscraper design, occurring mainly in Chicago in the 1880s and 1890s, was called the Functional period because skyscrapers were simple blocks with square frames. The second period was centered mainly in New York and lasted from about 1900 to 1920. It was called the Eclectic period. During this time shape and decoration became all the rage. Skyscraper architects borrowed ideas from the past, such as spires from Gothic cathedrals and columns from Roman temples. They designed some of the most remarkable skyscrapers of all time.

The Woolworth Building

Frank Winfield Woolworth (1852–1919) opened the first Woolworths store in 1879. By 1911 he owned over 600 stores, and had enough money to pay for his own skyscraper. The Woolworth Building was completed in 1913. It is 791 feet (241 m) high, and was the tallest building in the world until 1930 when the Bank of Manhattan Building rose to 927 feet (283 m). Its 55 stories are supported by a steel framework, but architect Cass Gilbert designed the outside to look like a stone-built Gothic cathedral. Marble walls and intricate ironwork decorate the inside.

Zoning Laws

In 1916 New York's city authorities introduced laws to restrict the size and shape of new skyscrapers. These tall buildings had begun to block out sunlight and air from the city's streets. The new laws meant that future buildings would have to gradually get thinner as they rose skyward.

New York Millionaires

At the beginning of the 20th century, hundreds of self-made millionaires lived in New York. They built grand mansions to live in and wanted grand buildings for their businesses, too. What better than a towering skyscraper to show off their success and status in society?

Right: Built in 1915, the 40-story Equitable Building on New York's Broadway was the bulkiest skyscraper in the city. It was the last high-rise to be built according to the old rules.

A cartoon-style carving of Frank Woolworth on the Woolworth Building.

Eclectic Decoration

During the Eclectic period, architectural styles came from many ages and places. Some skyscrapers were decorated, both inside and outside, like Gothic cathedrals with arches, spires, and gargoyles. Others resembled bell towers of the 14th century, or featured columns and reliefs (carved images on flat stone) copied from Greek or Roman temples.

Left: Millionaire Cornelius Vanderbilt's mansion in New York's fashionable 5th Avenue.

This statue called Civic Fame sits on the tallest spire of New York's Municipal Building.

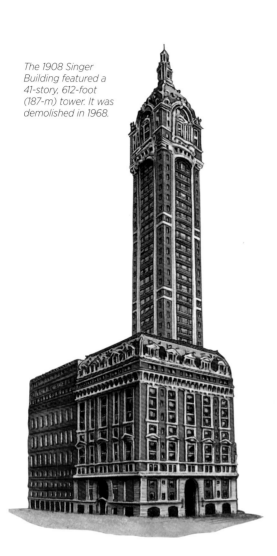

The 1908 Singer Building featured a 41-story, 612-foot (187-m) tower. It was demolished in 1968.

The distinctive 22-foot (7-m) wide clock on the Custom House Tower in Boston was added in 1915.

The Flatiron Building

New York's Flatiron Building is one of the city's most famous landmarks. Its triangular shape was forced on the architectural firm, D.H. Burnham & Co, by the shape of the building plot. It got its name because the triangle with its rounded end is similar to an old type of iron called a flatiron. Upon completion in 1903, the Flatiron Building stood 285 feet (87 m) high and many passers-by thought that it was so tall and thin it would collapse. The narrow end of the building was designed to look like a classical Greek column, and the walls copy architecture from French and Italian Renaissance buildings.

In the early 20th century, the Flatiron Building towered above the surrounding buildings on New York's streets.

"Cathedrals of Commerce"

When the Reverend Samuel Parkes Cadman, a Brooklyn minister, saw the Woolworth Building he was amazed by its beauty. He described it as the "Cathedral of Commerce." Just as Gothic cathedrals were monuments to God, the skyscrapers were monuments to business and capitalism. They were symbols of the power and wealth of their owners. Companies and city authorities began competing with each other to build the tallest skyscraper.

The Art Deco Period

The next period of skyscraper architecture lasted from about 1920 to 1940. It is known as the Art Deco period because skyscrapers were designed in the new and exciting Art Deco style. Skyscrapers became towering works of art. Skyscraper technology advanced too, with better materials and construction methods allowing skyscrapers to become taller and taller. Tallest of all was the Empire State Building, probably the most famous skyscraper of all time.

The Paris Exhibition

In 1925 an exhibition dedicated to modern decorative arts was held in Paris, France. Exhibitors came from all over the world. The exhibition had a worldwide impact. The term "Art Deco," used for the new style, came from the title of the exhibition—*Exposition Internationale des Arts Décoratifs et Industriels Modernes* (International Exhibit of Modern Decorative and Industrial Art).

The Empire State Building

The Empire State Building, completed in 1931, has 102 floors and measures 1,250 feet (381 m) to the top floor. It was the world's tallest building until 1973. Completed in just 410 days, at an average of four and a half floors every week, the workers who pieced together the steel frame worked at dizzying heights without safety equipment. The building was completed in the middle of America's worst economic depression and its offices were not filled until after World War II.

Over 3,000 men built the Empire State Building. They often risked their lives working on narrow platforms high above the city.

The mast tower was designed for mooring giant passenger airships, but was only used twice.

There are a total of 73 elevators in the Empire State Building.

The building's strength was tested in 1945 when a B-25 bomber flew accidentally into the 79th floor, killing 14 people and starting a fire.

About 15,000 people work in the building today.

The building's steel frame weighs 60,000 tons. Its total weight is 365,000 tons.

The building is clad in limestone and aluminum.

Steps known as setbacks required by city zoning laws.

Poster for the 1933 film King Kong, in which a giant ape climbs the Empire State Building, carrying the film's heroine with him.

A poster advertising the 1925 Paris arts exhibition.

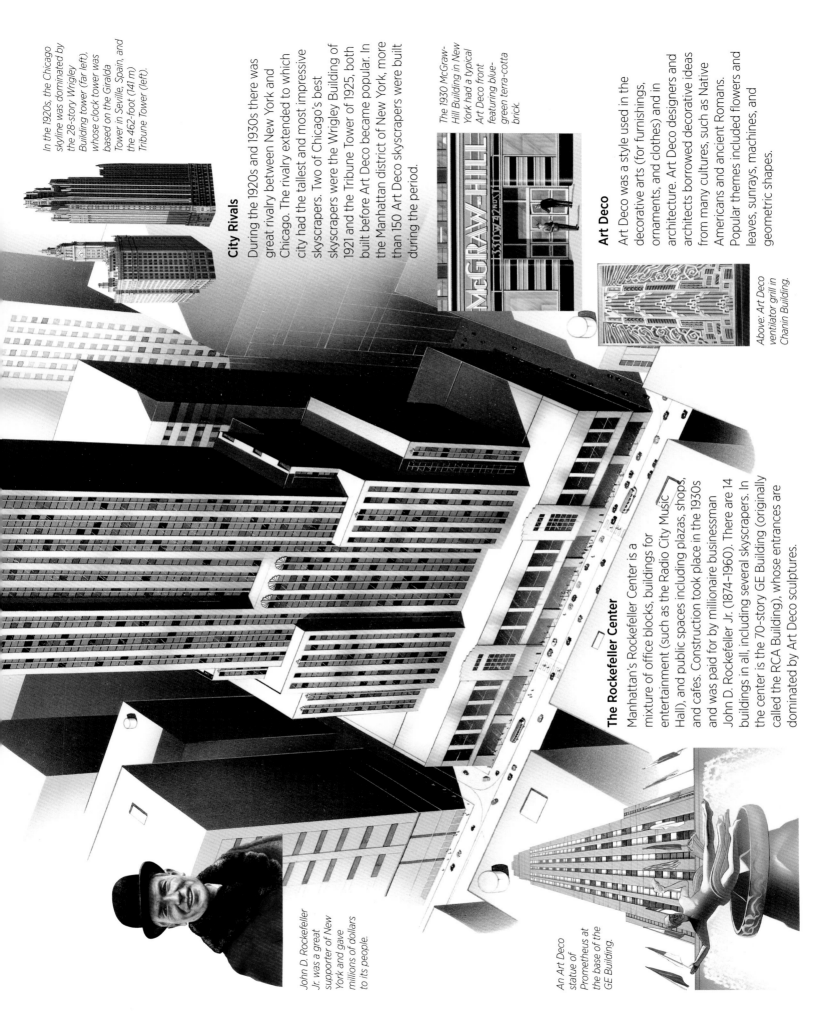

In the 1920s, the Chicago skyline was dominated by the 28-story Wrigley Building tower (far left), whose clock tower was based on the Giralda Tower in Seville, Spain, and the 462-foot (141 m) Tribune Tower (left).

City Rivals

During the 1920s and 1930s there was great rivalry between New York and Chicago. The rivalry extended to which city had the tallest and most impressive skyscrapers. Two of Chicago's best skyscrapers were the Wrigley Building of 1921 and the Tribune Tower of 1925, both built before Art Deco became popular. In the Manhattan district of New York, more than 150 Art Deco skyscrapers were built during the period.

The 1930 McGraw-Hill Building in New York had a typical Art Deco front featuring blue-green terra-cotta brick.

Art Deco

Art Deco was a style used in the decorative arts (for furnishings, ornaments, and clothes) and in architecture. Art Deco designers and architects borrowed decorative ideas from many cultures, such as Native Americans and ancient Romans. Popular themes included flowers and leaves, sunrays, machines, and geometric shapes.

Above: Art Deco ventilator grill in Chanin Building.

The Rockefeller Center

Manhattan's Rockefeller Center is a mixture of office blocks, buildings for entertainment (such as the Radio City Music Hall), and public spaces including plazas, shops, and cafes. Construction took place in the 1930s and was paid for by millionaire businessman John D. Rockefeller Jr. (1874–1960). There are 14 buildings in all, including several skyscrapers. In the center is the 70-story GE Building (originally called the RCA Building), whose entrances are dominated by Art Deco sculptures.

John D. Rockefeller Jr. was a great supporter of New York and gave millions of dollars to its people.

An Art Deco statue of Prometheus at the base of the GE Building.

The Chrysler Building

In the summer of 1929 the New York stock market was rising fast and gave no warning of the terrible crash that would take place in October. A property boom in the city saw dozens of new skyscrapers being built, and there was a fierce competition between the Chrysler Corporation and the Bank of Manhattan to build the world's tallest skyscraper. This was known as the "race to the sky." In 1930, Chrysler won with the 1046-foot (319-m) Chrysler Building, one of the finest Art Deco buildings in America.

The 927-foot (283-m) Bank of Manhattan Building (left), rival of the Chrysler Building (right).

On October 23, 1929 The 125-foot (38-m) stainless steel spire was hoisted onto the top of the Chrysler Building's dome bringing it to a height of 1046 feet (319 m).

❶ Spire
❷ Stainless steel crown
❸ Over 20,000 tons of structural steel were used
❹ Offices
❺ 77 stories
❻ Decoration is based on the hubcaps of Chrysler vehicles

Chrysler's Building Dream

Walter Chrysler (1875–1940) started his working life as a mechanic and quickly rose into management. In 1922 he started his own car-making company. In 1925 he founded the Chrysler Corporation, and later he decided to build a new headquarters in New York. He wanted the new building to put the Chrysler name on the map.

Walter Chrysler.

Architect William Van Alen wearing Chrysler Building fancy dress in 1931.

The Architect's Challenge

Walter Chrysler chose William Van Alen (1883–1954) to be his architect. He asked Van Alen to design the tallest building in the world. "Make this building higher than the Eiffel Tower," Chrysler told him. He also wanted a bold design that would reflect the modern machinery of the time—especially his cars. Van Alen designed an Art Deco building that would fulfil both of Chrysler's requests.

Symbol of the Modern Age

When it was completed the Chrysler Building took over from the Woolworth Building as the world's tallest skyscraper, and from the Eiffel Tower as the world's tallest structure. It appeared in adverts for Chrysler and its cars, and became a symbol of the great energy of New York City in the 1920s.

Right: The Chrysler Building appeared in this advertisement for Texaco Lubricant, used in the building's elevator system.

Building the Chrysler

Work on the Chrysler Building foundations started in September 1928, but the Bank of Manhattan Building was finished first. It stood two feet (60 cm) taller than the planned height of the Chrysler. However, Van Alen had a trump card. The Chrysler workers had secretly built a 180-foot (55-m) spire inside the top of the building, and now it was lifted into place. Chrysler had won the race. The Chrysler Building was built quickly and efficiently, and had an excellent safety record—no workers were killed during its construction.

Above: The first eight stories of the 21,000-ton steel frame of the Chrysler Building.

Two of the massive gargoyles decorating the Chrysler Building.

Chrysler Decoration

The Chrysler Building features extraordinary Art Deco decoration. Gargoyles on a motor theme, such as winged radiator caps and hubcaps, decorate the corners of the set-backs. On the 61st floor there are eight steel eagle heads. They are huge copies of the statuettes from Chrysler car bonnets. The building tapers to a four-sided spire decorated with stainless steel arches. In the lobby, marble, onyx, and amber murals show scenes from the Chrysler factory.

Giving up the Title

The Chrysler Building did not hold the title of the world's tallest building for long. Four months after it was finished it was overtaken by the Empire State Building. Its extraordinary style however, meant the Chrysler Building was not forgotten and it still remains a highlight of the New York skyline.

Left: Working on the Empire State Building with the Chrysler Building in the background.

The Chrysler Building's Art Deco elevator doors.

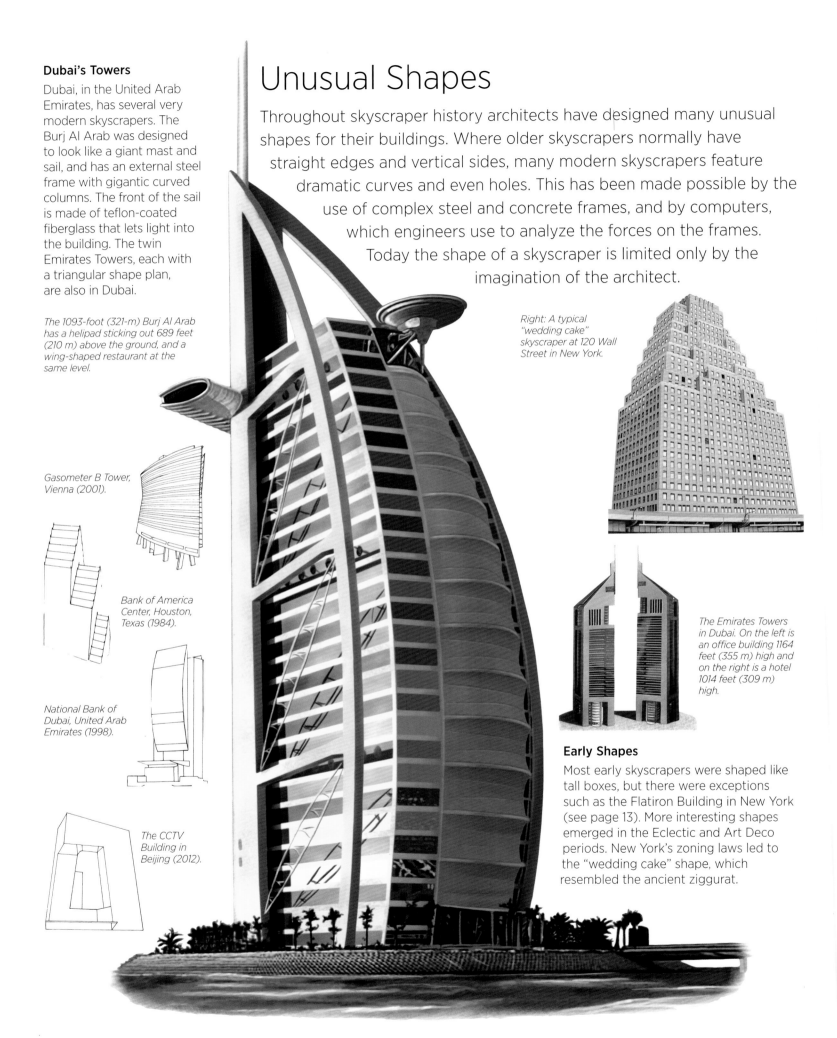

Dubai's Towers

Dubai, in the United Arab Emirates, has several very modern skyscrapers. The Burj Al Arab was designed to look like a giant mast and sail, and has an external steel frame with gigantic curved columns. The front of the sail is made of teflon-coated fiberglass that lets light into the building. The twin Emirates Towers, each with a triangular shape plan, are also in Dubai.

The 1093-foot (321-m) Burj Al Arab has a helipad sticking out 689 feet (210 m) above the ground, and a wing-shaped restaurant at the same level.

Gasometer B Tower, Vienna (2001).

Bank of America Center, Houston, Texas (1984).

National Bank of Dubai, United Arab Emirates (1998).

The CCTV Building in Beijing (2012).

Unusual Shapes

Throughout skyscraper history architects have designed many unusual shapes for their buildings. Where older skyscrapers normally have straight edges and vertical sides, many modern skyscrapers feature dramatic curves and even holes. This has been made possible by the use of complex steel and concrete frames, and by computers, which engineers use to analyze the forces on the frames. Today the shape of a skyscraper is limited only by the imagination of the architect.

Right: A typical "wedding cake" skyscraper at 120 Wall Street in New York.

The Emirates Towers in Dubai. On the left is an office building 1164 feet (355 m) high and on the right is a hotel 1014 feet (309 m) high.

Early Shapes

Most early skyscrapers were shaped like tall boxes, but there were exceptions such as the Flatiron Building in New York (see page 13). More interesting shapes emerged in the Eclectic and Art Deco periods. New York's zoning laws led to the "wedding cake" shape, which resembled the ancient ziggurat.

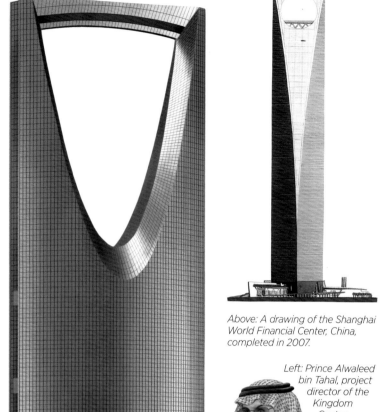

Barcelona's bullet-shaped Torre Agbar is 466 feet (142 m) high. Its outer glass walls contain solar cells that generate electricity for the building.

Ovals and Domes

Modern materials and engineering techniques allow buildings to have curved sides and roofs. A New York skyscraper (nicknamed the "Lipstick Building" because of its shape) breaks up the traditional straight lines on New York's streets. Its architect, Philip Johnson, described it as "an oval building in a square environment". Barcelona's Torre Agbar, designed by French architect Jean Nouvel, has a glass dome over the top floors that is a continuation of the walls.

Right: New York's Lipstick Building, completed in 1986, is one of the few round buildings in the city.

A Hole in the Middle

The spectacular Kingdom Center in Riyadh is one of the tallest buildings in Saudi Arabia. The tips of the two towers of this huge structure are joined by a 184-foot (56-meter) skybridge from which people can view the city below. The 1614-foot (492-m) tower of the Shanghai World Financial Center in China, which opened in 2008, has a huge hole in the top representing the sky. It also relieves wind pressure on the structure.

Above: A drawing of the Shanghai World Financial Center, China, completed in 2007.

Left: Prince Alwaleed bin Tahal, project director of the Kingdom Center.

Riyadh's Kingdom Center contains a hotel, apartments, a sports club, a wedding and conference centre and offices. It is clad in blue-colored glass.

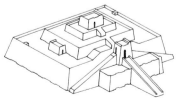

The Ziggurat of Ur (c.2000 B.C.).

The Taj Mahal, Agra, India (1643).

The Flatiron Building, New York (1903).

The Chrysler Building, New York (1930).

Wisma 46, Jakarta, Indonesia (1996).

The Al Faisaliah Complex in Riyadh, Saudi Arabia (2000).

Everyday Life of a Skyscraper

It is early morning and hundreds of workers are pouring into the lobby of a skyscraper. They line up for elevators that take them up to their offices. The skyscraper is like a self-contained town with restaurants, shops, a gym, and a dentist. When the working day ends the building empties again. Then a small army of cleaners and maintenance staff arrives. They clean the building, repair lighting and plumbing, and replenish stocks of food and other supplies. The building is ready for another day.

Many offices and meeting rooms in skyscrapers have fantastic views over the city and beyond.

Skyscraper Command

Every skyscraper has a command center from where the whole building is monitored. A bank of screens shows pictures from security cameras and gives information about the heating, air conditioning, plumbing, electricity usage, fire alarms, and communications. These services reach the floors through a central service core that runs the whole height of the building.

Duty officers monitor everything that goes on inside a skyscraper.

Offices and Apartments

The majority of skyscrapers are huge office blocks. A typical 50-story skyscraper, such as London's Canary Wharf Tower (see page 30), contains as much floor space as about 30 football pitches. The higher up the building an office is, the more expensive it is to rent. Some skyscrapers contain a mixture of offices and luxurious apartments. Chicago's John Hancock Center (see pages 26–27) for example, has offices up to the 41st floor followed by apartments to the 92nd floor, and a restaurant and observation deck at the top.

Tourist Attractions

Many skyscrapers are also tourist attractions. Some are visited because of their outstanding architecture, and others because they have public observation decks (see right) that offer fantastic views. Every day, about 5,000 visitors catch the non-stop elevators to the 103rd-floor Skydeck of the Sears Tower in Chicago, 1352 feet (412 m) above the city's streets (see pages 26–27).

The first Waldorf-Astoria Hotel (right) was demolished in 1929 to make way for the Empire State Building.

Left: This is the restaurant on the 53rd floor of the 656-foot (200-m) Main Tower in Frankfurt, Germany. Diners enjoy a fantastic view of the city below.

Hotels in the Sky

Skyscraper hotels offer residents great views over the city they are visiting. They are often expensive, luxury hotels with sumptuous decoration in the lobbies and restaurants, such as the Burj Al Arab in Dubai (see page 18). One of the oldest skyscraper hotels is the famous Waldorf-Astoria in New York, rebuilt in 1931.

Lunch and Leisure

When lunchtime arrives in a busy skyscraper, thousands of people flock to cafés and restaurants inside the building. Many skyscrapers have restaurants at the very top, where diners can enjoy the fantastic views along with their food. Some skyscrapers also contain health clubs, saunas, and gyms.

Elevators

A skyscraper would be completely useless without elevators to move people quickly between its floors. Skyscrapers have two sorts of elevators. Slow elevators stop at each floor. Express elevators carry people straight from the ground floor to observation decks. The Petronas Towers (see pages 40–41) has 76 elevators, 58 of which are double-decker elevators. Today, some companies are beginning to develop elevators that move both vertically and horizontally.

An advertisement for Otis Elevators in 1905.

Many office workers go to the gym in their lunch break.

Skyscraper window cleaners at work hundreds of feet above the pavement below.

Window Cleaning

Skyscrapers have a lot of windows! Keeping such a huge area of glass clean is not an easy job. Most skyscraper windows don't open, so they must be cleaned from the outside. Window cleaners work on cradles that dangle from gantries fixed to the lip of the roof. The Sears Tower has six wash robots that brush, rinse, and dry automatically.

Shopping

Skyscrapers such as the Citicorp Center in New York often contain shops or whole shopping centers. Some skyscrapers are even dedicated to shopping. The Lee Theatre Plaza in Hong Kong for example, is a 325-foot (99-m), 22-story shopping center.

The sign outside New York's Citicorp Center advertising the skyscraper's street-level department stores and restaurants.

The International Style

A building boom began in the early 1950s as the global economy recovered from World War Two. Art Deco, the style of the 1920s and 1930s, had gone. New skyscrapers were built in simple geometric shapes. They were clad in glass and metal, with almost no decoration. This new style was called the International Style, and it was to dominate the skyscraper world until the end of the 1960s. Many modern architects blame the International Style for cities full of dull, box-like skyscrapers.

The Style Spreads

The International Style was developed in the 1920s and 1930s by architects in western Europe, especially those at the Bauhaus design school in Germany. During the 1930s many people were forced to leave Europe by the rise of the Nazis in Germany. They included Walter Gropius and Ludwig Mies van der Rohe of the Bauhaus, who moved to America. This helped to spread the style worldwide. The term "International Style" came from the catalog of an architectural exhibition at New York's Museum of Modern Art in 1932. By the 1950s, the International Style dominated architecture.

Left: In 1921, Mies van der Rohe worked on an office building for Friedrichstrasse in Berlin. To be made entirely of glass, the proposed skyscraper was never built.

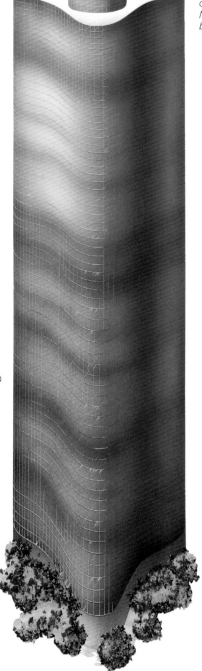

The Bauhaus

The Bauhaus (which means "house of construction" or "School of Building") was a German school of design founded in 1919 by architect Walter Gropius (1883–1969). Students at the school studied both art and craftsmanship. Ludwig Mies van der Rohe (1886–1969), the last director of the Bauhaus, was the most influential architect of the International Style. The Bauhaus closed in 1933.

Ludwig Mies van der Rohe.

Left: Lake Point Tower in Chicago was completed in 1968. Designed by Ludwig Mies van der Rohe, the apartment building stands 646 feet (197 m) tall.

Above: The Centro Pirelli in Milan, Italy was designed by Giovanni Ponti, often known as Gio Ponti, and completed in 1958. Standing 417 feet (127 m) tall, it was the second tallest building in Europe when built. Its floor plan is a long, thin hexagon.

Building International Style

The United Nations Secretariat Building and Lever House, both in New York and both completed in the early 1950s, were two of the first skyscrapers built in the International Style. Both are in the form of simple blocks. The United Nations skyscraper is 505 feet (154 m) tall and clad in green glass, marble, and bands of metal. Lever House, at 302 feet (92 m), is made up of two glass-and-steel blocks, one lying on the ground as a platform and the other standing vertically on it.

The emblem of the United Nations.

The United Nations Building, New York.

Below: Lever House, New York, has horizontal bands of glass and steel.

The Seagram Building in New York.

"Bauhaus"

Describing the Bauhaus not as an institution but as "an idea," Ludwig Mies van der Rohe explained why Bauhaus methods and practices had spread so widely around the world. From pottery, carpentry, and weaving to stagecraft and painting, Bauhaus students participated in a wide range of workshops under the instruction of some of the most skilled artists and craftspeople of the period. Products of these workshops were frequently put on display at exhibitions, such as the one at Weimar in 1923, and were reproduced around the world. The Bauhaus "idea" continues to influence art and architecture even today.

A postcard advertising the 1923 Bauhaus Exhibition.

The Seagram Building

New York's Seagram Building, completed in 1958, is considered to be the finest example of a skyscraper in the International Style. The Seagram Building is a simple block clad in glass, with vertical lines of bronze between the windows. It was designed by Ludwig Mies van der Rohe with Philip Johnson, and although copied many times, it was never bettered.

The New York Skyline

When we think of New York, we often think of the skyline of Manhattan, New York's central business area. This glittering skyline includes some of the most famous skyscrapers of all time, such as the Empire State Building and the Chrysler Building. There is an amazing range of architecture, from the Gothic tower of the Woolworth Building to modern, glass-clad skyscrapers. The skyline began to take shape in the early 1900s, gradually developing over the years to the one we know today.

The port of Manhattan as it was in 1750. This area is covered in skyscrapers today.

The Early Years

The Dutch settled in the area that is now New York in the early 1620s. They shared Manhattan Island with the Native Americans until they bought it in 1626. The small settlement became the city of New Amsterdam in 1653. It was captured by the English in 1664, who renamed it New York. Over the next century it became a busy port and trading center, and tripled in size.

A painted vase from about 1830 shows how New York's skyline looked then.

The Famous Skyline

If you look at a picture of New York in the late 19th century (see above), the tallest structures were the spires of churches. Just a hundred years later the same spires are lost in a jungle of skyscrapers (see below). New York's skyline has been famous since the 1930s, when immigrants from Europe viewed it with amazement. The tragic events of September 11, 2001 robbed the skyline of one of its most famous features, the Twin Towers, but they have been replaced by the new World Trade Center, including One World Trade Center, the tallest building in the Americas.

Above: A postcard of New York's three great Art Deco skyscrapers; the Chrysler Building, the Empire State Building, and the Rockefeller Center.

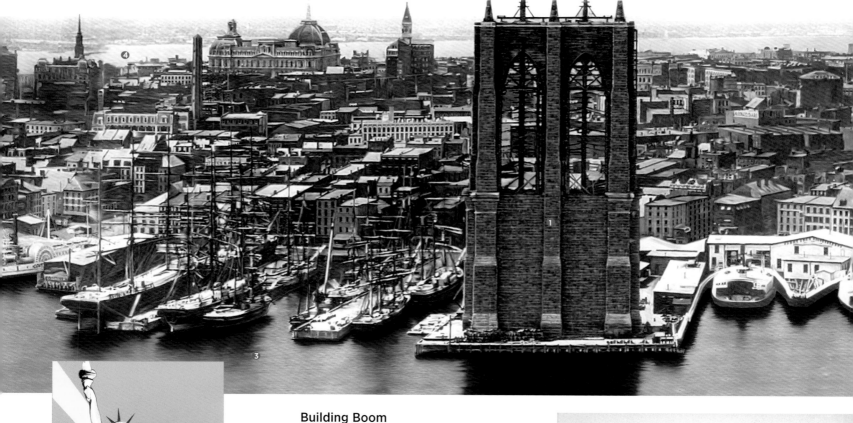

In the 1930s New York was nicknamed 'Wonder City of the World'.

Building Boom

New York was badly damaged during the American War of Independence (1775–81). The city was rebuilt, and new streets were laid out in a grid pattern. New York became the country's busiest port and commercial center. Millions of immigrants arrived from Europe in the second half of the 19th century and the early 20th century. The city grew fast. The first proper skyscrapers, such as the Flatiron Building (see page 13), began to appear in the early 20th century. They were a sign of the city's continuing commercial success.

Passengers on the ocean liner Queen Mary look at the New York skyline at dawn in 1939.

❶ Brooklyn bridge
❷ 120 Wall Street
❸ East River
❹ Hudson River
❺ South Street Seaport
❻ Chase Manhattan Building
❼ 60 Wall Street
❽ 70 Pine Street

Below: Brooklyn Bridge and part of Lower Manhattan in recent times.

The Supertall Period

In the mid-1960s the Empire State Building was still the world's tallest skyscraper, but a new race was about to begin. Companies and property developers all wanted to own the world's tallest building. This was the beginning of the Supertall Period, which lasted until the late 1970s. The towering new skyscrapers, such as the Sears Tower and the World Trade Center were made possible by the invention of new types of supporting frames.

The World Trade Center

The twin towers of the World Trade Center in New York (see page 36) were the tallest skyscrapers in the world when they were completed in 1973. One tower measured 1368 feet (417 m) and the other 1362 feet (415 m). Both had 110 stories. The towers had closely spaced steel columns around the outside, forming a strong tube structure, and also internal columns.

Tightrope walker Philippe Petit crossing a wire strung between the twin towers of the World Trade Center in 1974.

New Technology

The advanced technologies of the Supertall Period included new types of structures, materials such as high-grade steel, and the use of computer software to calculate the stresses and strains on frames. This saw the development of structures that were strong enough to support huge buildings, but which were lighter than the frames of smaller buildings of the past.

The tube-like frame (right) of the John Hancock Center (far right) in Chicago, has diagonal bracing to distribute the gravity load to all corners. Its tapered shape helps to reduce bending in high winds.

Wind Loads

The major problem for supertall buildings is the sideways push on the upper stories from strong winds. This push is called wind load. Strong winds try to bend a skyscraper over, making the top sway. This movement is called wind drift. A skyscraper frame must resist bending as well as holding up the weight inside.

The Sears Tower is the second tallest building in North America.

The Maine-Montparnasse Tower in Paris is 686 feet (209 m) high. Built in 1973, it was the tallest skyscraper in Europe at the time.

Fazlur Khan has been called the "Einstein of Structural Engineering."

Reaching New Heights

Structural engineer Fazlur Khan (1929–82) was one of the pioneers of the Supertall Period. He designed two of Chicago's great skyscrapers of the time, the 1129-foot (344-m) John Hancock Center, completed in 1969, and the Sears Tower. Their structures work like stiff tubes that resist bending from wind loads.

A movable piece of art by Alexander Calder (1898–1976), called Universe, stands in the lobby of the Sears Tower.

The Sears Tower

Completed in 1974, the Sears Tower in Chicago held the "world's tallest" record for more than 20 years. Standing 1453 feet (443 m) high, it was built as the headquarters of Sears, Roebuck and Company, and was one of the most innovative skyscrapers of its time. Its frame is made up of nine square tubes joined together, known as a "bundled tube," which is an extremely stiff structure. The tubes end at different heights, creating the building's set-backs.

Sears Tower Facts

The total floor space inside the Sears Tower is the same as 65 football pitches and there is enough steel in the building to make 50,000 cars. In a gale-force wind the top floor sways 3.2 feet (1 meter) from side to side. The building has its own post office. In 1999, Alain Robert, a French rock climber, nicknamed "Spiderman," climbed the outside of the Sears Tower.

27

Skyscrapers of the East

In the late 20th century there was unprecedented economic growth in the countries of East Asia. The main cities in the area expanded rapidly and thousands of new buildings sprang up, including many new skyscrapers. As in the past, cities and businesses built skyscrapers as symbols of their success, and in so doing built many of the world's tallest. East Asia has now taken over from the United States as the home of the supertall skyscraper.

Above: The Bank of China in Hong Kong was designed by the Chinese-born American architect I.M. Pei in 1982.

Economic Development

The "Asian miracle" began in Japan in the 1950s as Japan recovered from World War Two. In the 1960s and 1970s the economic success spread to Hong Kong, Singapore, Taiwan and South Korea. By the 1980s it had reached Malaysia, Thailand, and other countries. The boom was led by high-tech businesses and companies manufacturing electronic goods. Many Western companies switched manufacturing to Asia because of the low wages.

Battle for the Skies

There is fierce competition between the cities of East Asia to build the tallest skyscrapers. But height is not the only requirement. They are often designed to reflect the culture and religion of the area. Some of the finest examples are the Landmark Tower (above right) in Japan, the Petronas Towers (see pages 40–41), Taipei 101 (see pages 42–43), and Baiyoke II Tower in Bangkok which stands 997 feet (304 m) high.

Hong Kong

Hong Kong is home to many banks and financial institutions. Dozens of skyscrapers stand around the harbor of Hong Kong Island, including the International Commerce Center at 1588 feet (484 m) tall, Bank of China at 1210 feet (369 m) in height, Central Plaza which is 1227 feet (374 m) high, and the Hong Kong and Shanghai Bank (see pages 32–33). The Bank of China is made up of four triangular towers that end at different heights, each clad in silver reflective glass. The frame is made up of huge steel triangles.

Right: Japan's Landmark Tower was designed to resemble a traditional Japanese timber building. It stands 971 feet (296 m) tall against the backdrop of Mount Fujiyama.

Pilgrims' Building

The Tabung Haji Building in Kuala Lumpur is home to the organization that helps Muslims arrange their pilgrimage to Mecca in Saudi Arabia. The 499-foot (152-m) skyscraper is supported by five massive columns that represent the Five Pillars (basic beliefs) of Islam. The pilgrimage to Mecca, called the Hajj, is one of the Five Pillars of Islam.

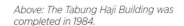

Above: The Tabung Haji Building was completed in 1984.

The Problem with Shanghai

With a population of over 20 million, Shanghai is China's largest city. Many skyscrapers have been built there in the last decades, including China's tallest, the Shanghai Tower (2073 feet/632 m), completed in 2014. In fact, there are so many skyscrapers in Shanghai that the soft ground is beginning to sink under their enormous weight. This has forced the authorities to cancel part of the city's massive building program.

Right: Shanghai's Jin Mao Tower (1381 feet/421 m) is now China's fourth tallest skyscraper.

The Hong Kong skyline is dominated by Two International Finance Center standing 1362 feet (415 m) high. Hong Kong became a British colony in 1842, but was returned to China in 1997.

Recent Styles

In the final decades of the 20th century, a number of different architectural styles were expressed in skyscrapers. The Postmodern Period began in the late 1970s. This style was an answer to the criticism about the dullness of the "glass box" skyscrapers of the International Style. It used architectural ideas from all over the world and from throughout history. Postmodern skyscrapers are found worldwide, while other skyscraper styles of the same period include Brutalism, Structural Expressionism, and High-Tech.

Commerzbank Headquarters

With its three corner towers, the headquarters of the 53-story German Commerzbank in Frankfurt is one of Norman Foster's most famous skyscrapers. At 850 feet (259 m) high, it was Europe's tallest building in 2004. It is also the world's first ecological skyscraper (see pages 34–35). All the offices and other internal spaces are lit by natural light, and each office has windows that can be opened. The building uses only half the energy of a standard skyscraper for lighting, heating, and cooling, and there are also gardens at various heights inside the building.

Postmodern Style

Postmodern style is made up of both ancient and modern ideas, with no rules, and where almost anything is possible. Postmodern skyscrapers come in an array of shapes and sizes, and are clad in a wide range of materials and colors. Typical Postmodern skyscrapers include the Messeturm in Frankfurt, the AT & T Building in New York, the Bank of America Center in Houston, Texas (see page 18), and the Canary Wharf Tower in London. Skylines of Postmodern skyscrapers can be seen in cities as far apart as Miami in Florida, Montreal in Canada, and Shanghai in China.

Standing 830 feet (253 m) high, the Rialto Towers in Melbourne, are the tallest office buildings in Australia.

Architect Cesar Pelli deliberately designed the Canary Wharf Tower (left) to be a simple form.

The Messeturm in Frankfurt, completed in 1990, resembles a medieval bell tower. The pyramid top is 118 feet (36 m) high.

Leading architects

Big names in modern skyscraper architecture include Philip Johnson, Cesar Pelli and Norman Foster. Philip Johnson, born in 1906, is thought of as the leader of Postmodernism. Many of his designs include daring features. His AT & T Building in New York is considered to be the first of the Postmodern skyscrapers. Cesar Pelli was the architect of the Petronas Towers (see pages 40–41), while Norman Foster designed the Commerzbank in Frankfurt, an example of Structural Expressionism.

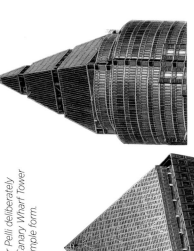

American architect Philip Johnson.

Structure of the Commerzbank

The Commerzbank has an interesting structure that is very different to most modern skyscrapers. It does not have an internal frame, but instead is supported by three giant towers, one at each corner of the triangular base. Elevators and other services go up the center of the columns. Banks of floors containing offices are supported between the columns by huge beams eight floors deep. In the center of the skyscraper is a full-height atrium (inner courtyard).

The Commerzbank is based on a triangular plan, but has a hollow center.

Completed in 1997, the Commerzbank is a distinctive feature of the Frankfurt skyline.

The top of the AT & T Building in New York is designed to look like a piece of Chippendale furniture.

The Hong Kong and Shanghai Bank

The headquarters of the Hong Kong and Shanghai Bank, completed in 1986, is one of the most impressive skyscrapers in Hong Kong. It is unlike most other skyscrapers because its supporting frame is visible from the outside. This gives it a high-tech, machine-like appearance. Standing 590 feet (180 m) high, its three individual stepped towers are 29, 36, and 44 stories tall.

The Bank

The Hong Kong and Shanghai Bank (HSBC) was founded in 1865, when trade between China and Europe was growing fast. It is now a major international bank, and the skyscraper is a symbol of the success of Hong Kong as a financial center.

One of two bronze lions outside the Hong Kong and Shanghai Bank. They are symbols of prosperity.

Architect Sir Norman Foster is renowned for his use of new materials and high technology in his building designs.

A New Home

In 1979 the directors of the Hong Kong and Shanghai Bank decided that they needed a new headquarters. They wanted the "best banking building in the world," and asked seven leading international architects to submit proposals for a new building. They chose British architect Sir Norman Foster for the job.

The Hong Kong and Shanghai Bank was the ex-colony's first bank. Part of an early banknote (above).

The original bank building on a banknote of 1976. The building was demolished to make way for the new one.

1 ❶ ROOF
2 ❷ VIEWING GALLERY
3 ❸ GARDEN TERRACE
4 ❹ CLEAR GLASS COVERS MOST OF THE BUILDING
5 ❺ STEEL COVERING
6 ❻ OFFICES
7 ❼ 12-STORY ATRIUM
8 ❽ MANY PARTS OF THE BANK WERE PREFABRICATED
9 ❾ MAIN BANKING HALL
10 ❿ ESCALATORS
11 ⓫ ENTRANCE HALL
12 ⓬ BASEMENT
13 ⓭ MAINTENANCE ROOMS, VAULTS, TRUCK BAYS, AND PARKING AREAS

Construction

The Hong Kong and Shanghai Bank was completed over a period of three years. The job was a difficult one to organize because of the small site and its location in the busy city. Engineers solved the problem by making large parts of the building off site and only bringing them in when they were needed. This way of building is called prefabrication. Workers followed 120,000 drawings as they pieced the building together, working 24 hours a day.

Above: Steel erectors guiding a piece of steel frame into place on the Hong Kong and Shanghai Bank.

Left: A collection of mirrors, called a sun scoop, reflect sunlight into the building's atrium. This external reflector follows the sun across the sky.

Building a Skyscraper

Before an architect begins to design a skyscraper, the uses of the building must be established and the site chosen. Architects work with engineers and other professionals to insure that all aspects of the building will work properly together. Once all the parts are designed, construction begins. Foundations, which connect the building with the ground, are built first. Then the frame goes up. Floors are added as the frame rises, followed by cladding. Once a floor is weatherproof, services such as electrics and plumbing are added. The lower floors are often complete before the frame for the upper floors is finished. Hundreds of specialist workers, from steel erectors and crane drivers to plumbers and decorators, are needed for the job.

Work on building the bank began in 1983 and the foundations were dug by hand. By January 1984, the building was complete to level 26.

33

Coping with the Natural World

Soaring high above city streets, skyscrapers are in the way of the worst of the weather. They are battered by strong winds, lashed by rain, snow, and hail, hit by lightning, and exposed to extremes of temperature. In some areas of the world they can be shaken by earthquakes too. But skyscrapers are designed to withstand anything that nature throws at them. They are some of the safest buildings in the world.

The Torre Mayor in Mexico City. Built in 2002, it is 738 feet (225 m) high, and sits on soft soil, but has piles that reach down to solid rock. In 1985 an earthquake in Mexico City saw over 600 buildings collapse.

US Bank Tower

Scientists think that a major earthquake, nicknamed the "Big One," could strike Los Angeles at any time. The 1018 foot (310-m) US Bank Tower (left), completed in 1990, stands just 26 miles (42 km) from the San Andreas fault, but it is designed to withstand a major earthquake. It has an extremely strong central core and lighter side columns. Together they make a lightweight but flexible frame.

Left: If an earthquake struck Los Angeles, the side-to-side shaking of the ground would pass up the US Bank Tower in waves, leaving the structure undamaged. In this illustration we can see the US Bank Tower's response to an earthquake. A completely solid building would be shaken apart.

Building in earthquake zones

Some of the world's tallest skyscrapers are in cities in major earthquake zones, such as San Francisco, Mexico City and Tokyo. These skyscrapers are designed to resist the sideways shaking from an earthquake. A very strong frame is used, but one that allows the building to bend and sway, absorbing the energy from the earthquake. Rubber pads between the frame and foundations also reduce vibrations, while deep foundations stop skyscrapers built on soft soil from toppling over.

The 853-foot (260-m) Transamerica Building in San Francisco was undamaged by a severe earthquake in 1989. Its flexible frame is isolated from its deep foundations by shock absorbers, and its triangular shape makes it very stable.

San Francisco and Los Angeles are close to the San Andreas Fault, where the edges of two huge tectonic plates slide past each other. An earthquake here flattened much of San Francisco in 1906.

What is an Earthquake?

Earthquakes take place because the Earth's crust is cracked into many pieces, which are moving very slowly. The cracks are called faults. The biggest faults are between huge pieces of the crust called tectonic plates, and this is where the worst earthquakes happen. As the edges of the plates move, they often get caught against each other. The stress on the rocks gradually builds up until they move with a sudden jolt, causing an earthquake. Energy, in the form of seismic waves, spreads out through the surrounding rocks. As the waves pass, the ground shakes violently from side to side.

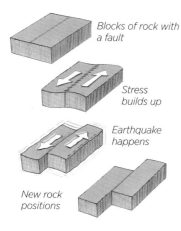

Blocks of rock with a fault

Stress builds up

Earthquake happens

New rock positions

Lightning

Skyscrapers are often hit by lightning during storms. It is said that lightning strikes the Empire State Building about 100 times each year. Most skyscrapers have lightning rods on their rooftops, which are designed to direct a lighting bolt to the ground.

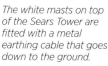

The white masts on top of the Sears Tower are fitted with a metal earthing cable that goes down to the ground.

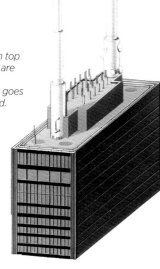

Environmental Sustainability

Many of the latest skyscrapers are designed to be environmentally friendly. They use less energy for heating, cooling, and lighting than traditional skyscrapers. All the offices in the Commerzbank headquarters (see pages 30–31) are lit by natural light, and air flows up naturally through the building to keep it cool. Designers are also trying to incorporate such ideas as windows you can open and recycling the interior heat of buildings in an effort to make them more comfortable and ecologically sound.

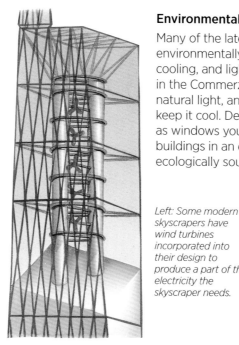

Left: Some modern skyscrapers have wind turbines incorporated into their design to produce a part of the electricity the skyscraper needs.

Below: A section of skyscraper cladding is being tested to check if it is watertight in simulated typhoon conditions.

Wind Resistance

Skyscrapers are designed to resist the strongest winds. In some places these are hurricane winds of more than 149 mph (240 km/h). Skyscrapers sometimes have diagonal bracing in addition to a frame of beams and columns, while the central core plays a major part in supporting the building. However, all skyscrapers sway slightly in very strong winds. The Citicorp Center in New York has a 400 ton concrete block in the top that moves automatically to counteract swaying.

Left: The ventilation system in the Commerzbank headquarters.

Extreme Temperatures

Many parts of North America face freezing winters and very hot summers, while overheating in skyscrapers is a big problem in hot and humid countries like Malaysia and Saudi Arabia. Machinery, office equipment, and people all give out heat, and windows trap heat from the sun like a giant greenhouse. Double- and triple-glazing, air conditioning systems, and heat-reflecting glass cladding help maintain the temperature inside a skyscraper. All the windows in the National Commerce Bank (right) in Jeddah, Saudi Arabia face inward into huge holes in the building, where they are shaded from direct sunlight.

Built in 1984, the National Commerce Bank has no windows on the outside.

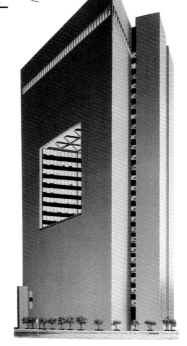

The World Trade Center

September 11, 2001 will always be remembered as the date when the twin skyscrapers of the World Trade Center were destroyed in a terrorist attack. The Twin Towers, as they were known, were a major symbol of the financial power of the Uniated States. When they were completed in the early 1970s, they were the world's tallest skyscrapers, although they soon lost the title to the Sears Tower. There were many ideas about what to do with the World Trade Center site following September 11. In 2004 it was decided to undertake plans for developing the area. A new skyscraper, called One World Trade Center, would be its centerpiece.

The Twin Towers stood in Manhattan on the shores of New York Bay.

Skyscraper Tragedies

September 11 was neither the first attack on the Twin Towers, nor the first skyscraper tragedy. In 1993 a bomb was set off in the underground car park of one of the Twin Towers. It blew a huge hole in the basement and rocked the tower, killing six people and injuring hundreds more. In 1945 a B-25 bomber, lost in fog, flew into the Empire State Building, killing 13 people.

Fire at the top of the Ostankino TV Tower, Moscow in 2000. Four people died.

September 11

The terrorist attack on the Twin Towers happened on the morning of 11 September 2001. At 8.50 a.m. a hijacked passenger plane was flown into the north tower. Another plane was flown into the south tower 14 minutes later. The planes' fuel started intense fires. At 10.05 a.m. the south tower collapsed. The other tower collapsed at 10.28 a.m. Over 2,700 people were killed, including hundreds of firefighters and police officers.

The Twin Towers soon after the south tower was hit by the second plane.

The Twin Towers

The Twin Towers were at the heart of the huge World Trade Center complex, and were officially called One World Trade Center (north tower) and Two World Trade Center (south tower). Designed by American architect Minoru Yamasaki (1912–86), the offices of the Twin Towers were rented by hundreds of international companies.

A World Trade Center memorial ribbon, sold to raise funds for the victims of September 11.

Why Did the Twin Towers Collapse?

It seems incredible that the Twin Towers could collapse so catastrophically. Architects and engineers knew there was always a possibility of the towers being hit accidentally by a plane, and they designed them to withstand a huge impact. So what went wrong? The answer is that when the planes hit the towers on 11 September they were fully laden with fuel. The fires caused by the fuel created temperatures so high that the steel frames became weak and buckled. They could not hold up the floors above, which then fell, crushing the floors underneath.

After the Attacks

In the days after the attack, the authorities concentrated on searching for the thousands of people who were missing. Rescuers worked round the clock at the site, which became known as "Ground Zero." In the meantime, the US Government declared a "war on terror." They invaded Afghanistan, from where they believed the terrorist group responsible, called al-Qaida, and its leader, Osama bin Laden, had organized the attack. Al-Qaida training bases were destroyed, and Osama bin Laden was finally caught and killed in 2011.

Rescue workers put up the American flag at Ground Zero.

Memorial Competition

As the rubble was cleared from Ground Zero there was much discussion about what should happen to the site. Some people wanted to rebuild the Twin Towers. Others wanted the site to be left as a memorial. In December 2002 nine new proposals from world-renowned architects were studied. In February 2003, two finalists were chosen: one by Daniel Libeskind and the other from an international team called Think. Each design included a space for a memorial.

Architect Daniel Libeskind has designed some of the world's most unusual buildings.

Above: The design for the World Trade Center site put forward by the Think team. At its center are two transparent towers.

Winning Designs

In February 2003 a winner was announced for the World Trade Center site. It was a design by Polish-American architect Daniel Libeskind. At its center is a skyscraper called One World Trade Center which, at 1776 feet (541.4 m) high, is North America's tallest building. This building was designed with David Childs, the architect chosen by the site's property developer. The height in feet is the same figure as the date of America's Declaration of Independence (1776). In January 2004, architect Michael Arad's design for a memorial on the site of the Twin Towers was chosen from over 5,000 entries.

Above: On the exact spots where the Twin Towers stood there are two memorial pools, with the names of all the victims of September 11 inscribed on a bronze parapet. The memorial, by architect Michael Arad, is called the National 9/11 Memorial.

Artist's impression of how the entire complex at Ground Zero will look when completed.

Into The 21st Century

Throughout the 1990s many plans appeared for weird, wonderful, and supertall skyscrapers that were to be built to commemorate the new Millennium. A few were built, but many remained on the drawing board, perhaps to be built some time in the future. Skyscrapers continue to be built in the 21st century and the reasons for building them remain the same as they always were. These are to create living space in rapidly-growing cities, to create office space in expensive city centers, and to boost the egos of their owners.

The Eiffel Tower during the Millennium eve celebrations.

The Millennium Tower would have stood on its own purpose-built island in Tokyo Bay in Japan, surrounded by a marina.

The Millennium Tower

One of the most ambitious plans for a skyscraper for the Millennium was the Millennium Tower, designed by Sir Norman Foster. Unfortunately, it was never built, but it may be in the future. Measuring a staggering 2756 feet (840 m) in height, the Millennium Tower would have been the tallest structure in the world. It would have had 170 floors, with offices, hotels, and apartments on different levels. With space for 52,000 people, it would have been like a self-contained mini city. It was designed with a helical steel cage frame to make it both hurricane and earthquake proof.

The Millennium Tower would have been accessible by a high-speed train line connecting it to the mainland.

Left: Norman Foster and partner with a model of the Millennium Tower.

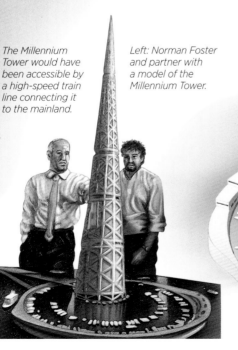

London's Swiss Re Headquarters is 591 (180 m) high and has a grid-like perimeter frame.

Right: Completed in 2000, Aurora Place stands 719 feet (219 m) high in downtown Sydney.

Conflict and Progress

Supertall buildings are not welcomed by everybody, especially in historic city centers. The Eiffel Tower, completed more than a hundred years ago, is still the tallest structure in Paris. The Parisians are proud of their old buildings, and many oppose the construction of modern skyscrapers. In London, the new headquarters of the Swiss Re company was the first tall skyscraper to be built in the city after 1980. This round, glass-clad tower is lit by natural light and cooled by natural ventilation.

Blending In

The arrival of the 21st century brought new challenges for architects. Many cities rejected skyscraper proposals which would completely change the look of their skyline. The proposed 730-foot (223-m) high Heron Building in London for example, was subject to a public enquiry after it was said it would spoil the view of St. Paul's Cathedral. In Sydney however, architect Renzo Piano's curved design of the Aurora Place skyscraper blended in well with the world-famous Sydney Opera House.

Building Boom

Skyscraper building is still in full-swing in the 21st century. The big growth area is Asia and the Pacific, but skyscrapers are shooting up in cities across the United States, Europe, Asia, and the Middle East. These skyscrapers include very high-tech features in their construction, climate control, communications, and safety. Examples include the IDX Tower in Seattle, completed in 2002, and the tower of the Sony Center in Berlin, completed in 2000. Many of the latest skyscrapers are also designed to be environmentally friendly, using natural lighting and ventilation to reduce energy use.

The 338 foot (103 m) skyscraper at the new Sony Center in Berlin, designed by architect Helmut Jahn.

The 41-story EDF Tower, completed in 2001, is one of the few skyscrapers in Paris.

The Sydney Opera House, opened in 1973, is one of the most famous buildings in Australia.

The Petronas Towers

The magnificent Petronas Towers in Kuala Lumpur, Malaysia, were the world's tallest skyscrapers between 1996 and 2004. Each of the twin towers stands 1483 feet (452 m) tall. For the first time the "world's tallest" title left the United States. The Petronas Towers were built by Petronas (Malaysia's national oil company), the Malaysian government, and other investors to show off Malaysia's growing commercial success, its culture, and Islamic traditions. In 2004 however, they were overtaken by Taipei 101 in Taiwan.

Standing Tall

The Petronas Towers were designed by the Argentinean-born architect Cesar Pelli. His architectural firm, Cesar Pelli & Associates, was asked to reflect Malaysia's traditional buildings and culture, while also considering the country's climate. The towers are based on geometric patterns. The floorplan is made up of two squares superimposed, forming an eight-pointed star, with small arcs filling the angles. Inside, the frame is made up of a reinforced concrete core and an outer ring of columns, forming a super-stiff structure.

Cesar Pelli, the man behind the design of the Petronas Towers.

The Petronas Towers are clad in glass, aluminum and stainless steel. They resemble traditional Malaysian temple towers.

1. SPIRE
2. CROWN
3. GROUND FLOOR
4. OUTER RING OF COLUMNS
5. DOUBLE-DECKER ELEVATORS
7. ESCALATORS
8. RECEPTION AREA
9. GEOMETRIC FLOOR PLAN

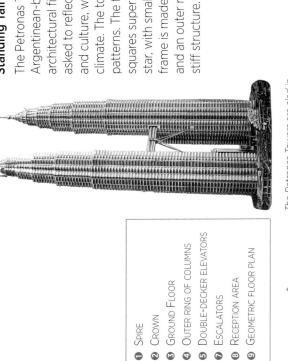

Looking at one of the towers from top to bottom.

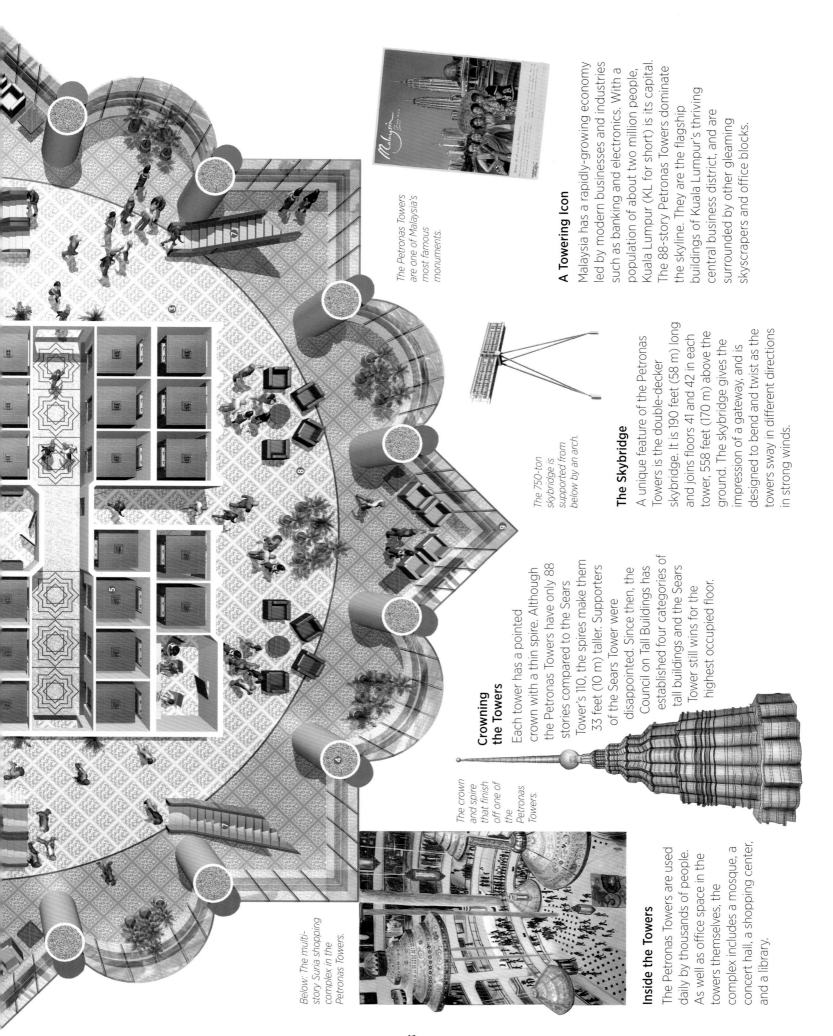

The Petronas Towers are one of Malaysia's most famous monuments.

A Towering Icon

Malaysia has a rapidly-growing economy led by modern businesses and industries such as banking and electronics. With a population of about two million people, Kuala Lumpur (KL for short) is its capital. The 88-story Petronas Towers dominate the skyline. They are the flagship buildings of Kuala Lumpur's thriving central business district, and are surrounded by other gleaming skyscrapers and office blocks.

The 750-ton skybridge is supported from below by an arch.

The Skybridge

A unique feature of the Petronas Towers is the double-decker skybridge. It is 190 feet (58 m) long and joins floors 41 and 42 in each tower, 558 feet (170 m) above the ground. The skybridge gives the impression of a gateway, and is designed to bend and twist as the towers sway in different directions in strong winds.

Crowning the Towers

Each tower has a pointed crown with a thin spire. Although the Petronas Towers have only 88 stories compared to the Sears Tower's 110, the spires make them 33 feet (10 m) taller. Supporters of the Sears Tower were disappointed. Since then, the Council on Tall Buildings has established four categories of tall buildings and the Sears Tower still wins for the highest occupied floor.

The crown and spire that finish off one of the Petronas Towers.

Inside the Towers

The Petronas Towers are used daily by thousands of people. As well as office space in the towers themselves, the complex includes a mosque, a concert hall, a shopping center, and a library.

Below: The multi-story shopping complex Suria in the Petronas Towers.

The World's Tallest

From before the Egyptian pharaohs built their pyramids, height has been a symbol of importance and power in the building world. Today, countries, cities and companies compete for the prestige of owning the world's tallest skyscraper. Unfortunately, there are constant arguments about how skyscrapers should be measured, and which skyscraper really is the tallest. For much of the 20th century the title was held by buildings in the United States, but now some of the world's tallest buildings are being constructed in Asia and The Middle East.

The spire gave Taipei 101 the extra height it needed to be the world's number one.

Taipei 101's shape is supposed to reflect the shape of a bamboo stalk.

Very fast elevators carry visitors to the 90th floor in 39 seconds.

Skyscraper Wars

The competition for the "world's tallest" has been going on for more than a hundred years. The title changed hands many times in the early 20th century as powerful American businessmen built their own skyscrapers. Competition was fiercest in the 1920s, in a battle between the Chrysler company and the Bank of Manhattan (see pages 16–17). The Chrysler Building won, but it was soon overtaken by the Empire State Building, which held the title for 40 years.

The Woolworth Building, seen here with the Brooklyn Bridge, was the tallest building in the world for only 17 years.

The Brooklyn Daily Eagle reported the opening of the Empire State Building, the world's tallest building, in May 1931.

What Makes a Tall Building?

The "world's tallest building" title is always held by a skyscraper because a building is defined as a structure with an enclosed interior designed for working or living in. This excludes many communications towers, such as the CN Tower, that are taller than any skyscrapers. The Council on Tall Buildings has introduced new categories to try to stop the arguments over which skyscraper is tallest. These are: the height to architectural top, the height to highest occupied floor, the height to top of the roof, and the height to the top of an antenna.

The CN Tower in Toronto, Canada, was the world's tallest structure at 1815 feet (553 m), but it was not classified as a building.

The Tallest in the World

Some of the world's tallest skyscrapers, present and future, are shown in the diagram on page 43. The order of heights of these buildings is generally agreed, but many disagree with the list because of the use of spires and aerials to gain extra height. The list includes the Empire State Building, which is more than 70 years old, and the Freedom Tower which is planned for 2008. In ten years time however, this diagram will probably look very different.

Bank of China, Hong Kong.

Central Plaza, Hong Kong.

Empire State Building, New York.

Shun Hing Square, Shenzhen, China.

Sky Central Plaza, Guangzhou, China.

Two International Finance Centre, Hong Kong.

Jin Mao Tower, Shanghai.

Sears Tower, Chicago.

Petronas Towers, Kuala Lumpur.

Shanghai World Financial Center, Shanghai.

Taipei 101, Taipei, Taiwan.

One World Trade Center, New York..

Taipei 101

In October 2003, a 197-foot (60-m) spire was attached to the top of the Taipei 101 skyscraper in Taipei, Taiwan, giving the building a height of 1667 feet (508 m). At that moment it became the world's tallest skyscraper, beating the Petronas Towers in Kuala Lumpur, Malaysia (see pages 40–41). The "101" in the name is the number of floors the building has. However, it very soon lost its title, as new, taller skyscrapers were built around the world.

Images of Taipei 101 appear all over Taiwan, even on buses! The country is proud of having the world's tallest building.

The entrance to the main lobby of Taipei 101.

The low-rise building contains a shopping centre, leisure areas and a conference hall.

The foundations and frame are both earthquake and typhoon proof.

Designs for the Future

Not all proposed skyscrapers get built. This page shows some recently constructed skyscrapers, as well as some that were planned but will never be built. The Grollo Tower, designed by architect Harry Seidler, was to be supported by six huge tapering columns that were part of an external frame. In the London Bridge Shard, excess heat from lower-floor offices heats apartments on the upper floors. The Scandinavian Tower, an 85-story hotel planned for Malmö in Sweden and nicknamed "the bootleg," was to get wider at the top. Meanwhile, planners in Dubai have proposed the Dubai City Tower, which would have 400 stories and stand 1.5 miles (2.4 km) tall, and would be a sort of "vertical city."

These plans show the variety of architectural styles of the modern skyscraper.

The Burj Khalifa, also known as the Burj Dubia, in Dubai, United Arab Emirates stands at 2722 feet (830 m) and is currently the tallest building in the world.

The Grollo Tower, in Melbourne, Australia, will never see the light of day. Originally planned at 2224 feet (678 m), it would have been one of the tallest buildings in the world.

The Scandinavian Tower, Malmö, Sweden, was never built. It would have been the tallest building in Europe.

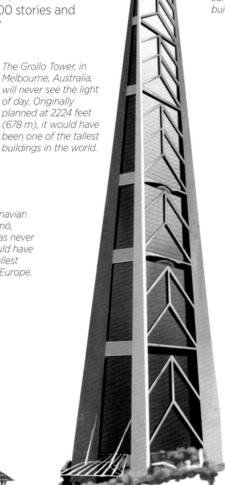

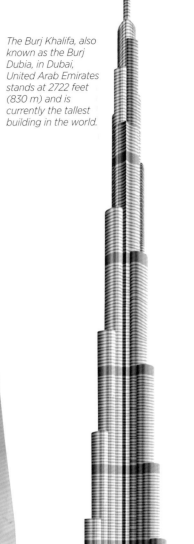

The Shard, also known as the Shard of Glass, or the Shard London Bridge, in London England, was completed in 2012. At 1004 feet (306 m), it is currently the tallest building in the European Union.

Future Plans

The terrorist attacks on the World Trade Center in 2001 made many people think that the days of the supertall skyscraper were over. However, construction has of new skyscrapers has continued, and there are many extraordinary "superscrapers" on the drawing boards of architects' offices around the world. Skyscrapers will always be needed to create living and working space as the population grows. But just how tall will skyscrapers become? Engineers say there is no real limit on height. It just depends on whether developers are willing to pay the enormous construction costs of mega skyscrapers and whether people can feel comfortable so high up.

World-renowned Italian architect Renzo Piano designed the London Bridge Tower, nicknamed the Shard.

Elephant and Castle Eco-Tower, London, England.

HUMAN POPULATION

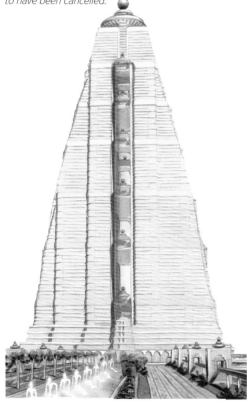

There are currently four times as many people on the planet as there were when the first skyscrapers were built just over one hundred years ago. The population is estimated to grow to around ten billion by 2050.

Plans for a 2222-foot (677-m) pyramid-shaped skyscraper called the World Centre for Vedic Learning were announced in India by Maharishi Mahesh Yogi in 1998. The project seems to have been cancelled.

A Place in the Future?

Despite people's doubts about skyscrapers after September 11, skyscrapers are here to stay. Architects argue that the World Trade Center was attacked because it was a symbol of the USA's economic and political power, not because it was a skyscraper. However, the same architects are rethinking skyscraper design, and future skyscrapers are likely to have better protection against fire, better escape routes, and better access for emergency workers. The world's population is increasing rapidly, and most people will live in cities. Skyscrapers may be the only way to make space for everybody.

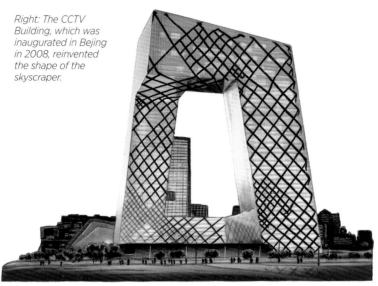

Right: The CCTV Building, which was inaugurated in Bejing in 2008, reinvented the shape of the skyscraper.

Skyscrapers of the Future

What will a typical skyscraper of the future look like? It is hard to say, especially as there is no typical skyscraper of today! There is a movement toward environmentally friendly skyscrapers, which will save energy and be pleasant and comfortable to work and live in. But what about the headline-grabbing skyscraper feature —height? With continuing advances in materials and frame designs, there really is no limit. Even back in 1956, architect Frank Lloyd Wright proposed a mile-high needle-like skyscraper.

Fiction or Reality?

A quick surf on the Internet will throw up dozens of proposals for incredible skyscrapers, some with heights of more than 2000 feet (600 m). It is hard to know how many of these proposals will ever get off the drawing board and become a reality. Many past plans have not, usually because they would have been so expensive to build that the developers would never have got their money back through renting the space inside.

The skyline of Hong Kong will always be dominated by supertall skyscrapers.

A proposal for 7 South Dearborn Street in Chicago, which would have been 1552 feet (473 m) high.

Index

Afghanistan 36
Al-Qaida 36
America 7, 8, 10, 11, 13, 14, 15, 16, 22, 25, 26, 28, 35, 36, 37, 39, 40, 42, 45
– Boston 13
– Chicago 7, 10, 11, 12, 15, 20, 21, 22, 26, 27, 43, 45
– Houston 18, 30
– Los Angeles 34
– Miami 30
– New York 7, 10, 11, 12, 13, 14, 15, 16, 17, 18, 19, 21, 22, 23, 24–25, 26, 30, 31, 35, 36, 43
– San Francisco 34
– Seattle 39
American War of Independence 25
Arad, Michael 37
Architectural periods
– Art Deco Period 7, 14–15, 16, 17, 18, 25
– Brutalism 30
– Eclectic Period 12–13, 18
– Functional Period 12
– High-Tech 30
– International Style 22–23, 30
– Postmodern Period 30
– Structural Expressionism 30
– Supertall Period 26–27
Asia 7, 28, 29, 39
Australia 30, 39, 44
– Melbourne 30, 44
– Sydney 39
Austria
– Vienna 18

Bank of Manhattan 16, 42
Bauhaus Design School 22, 23
Brooklyn Bridge, New York 42
Brooklyn Daily Eagle 42
Bruegel the Elder, Pieter 8
Burma 9
Burnham, D.H. and Co. 13
Burnham, Daniel 11

Cadman, rev Samuel Parkes 13
Calder, Alexander 27
Canada 30, 42
– Montreal 30
– Toronto 42
Cathedrals 8, 12, 13
Cesar Pelli & Associates 40
Chicago School 10, 11
Childs, David 37
China 19, 28, 29, 30, 32, 43
– Guangzhou 43
– Hong Kong 7, 21, 28–29, 32, 33, 43, 45
– Peking 18, 45
– Shanghai 29, 30, 43
– Shenzhen 43
– Singapore 28
Chrysler Corporation 16, 42
Chrysler, Walter 16
Churches 8, 25
Council on Tall Buildings 40, 41, 42

Earthquakes 7, 34, 35, 43
Egypt 8, 9
– Cairo 9
– Giza 9
– Saqqara 9
Eiffel, Gustave 9
Elevators 7, 11, 14, 16, 17, 20, 21, 42

England 9, 44
– London 9, 20, 30, 39, 44
Environmental sustainability 31, 35, 39, 45
Europe 7, 8, 25, 32, 39

Five Pillars of Islam 29
Foster, sir Norman 30, 31, 32, 33, 38
France 9, 14
– Paris 14, 26, 39
Freedom Gardens, New York 37

Germany 21, 22
– Berlin 22, 39
– Frankfurt 21, 30, 31
Gilbert, Cass 12
Great Mosque of Samarra 8
Gropius, Walter 22, 23
Ground Zero, New York 36, 37
Guatemala 9
– Tikal 9

Hajj 29

India 19, 45
– Agra 19
Indonesia 19, 28
– Jakarta 19
Iraq 8, 9
– Babylon 8
– Samarra 8
– Ur 9
Italy 8, 22
– Milan 22
– Pisa 8
– Rome 8
– San Gimignano 8
– Venice 8

Jahn, Helmut 39
Japan 28, 29, 38
– Mount Fujiyama 29
– Tokyo 34, 38
Jenney, William Le Baron 10, 11
Johnson, Philip 19, 23, 30

Khan, Fazlar 26, 27
King Kong 14

Laden, Osama bin 36
Libeskind, Daniel 37
Lightning 34, 35

Malaysia 28, 35, 40, 41, 43
– Kuala Lumpur 29, 40, 41, 43
Mexico 9
– Chichen Itzà 9
– Mexico City 34
Mies van der Rohe, Ludwig 22, 23
Minarets 8

Nouvel, Jean 19

Otis, Elisha 11

Pacific Ocean 39
Pagodas 8, 9
– Shwe Dagon Pagoda, Burma 9
Pei, I.M. 28
Pelli, Cesar 30, 40
Petit, Philippe 26
Piano, Renzo 39, 44
Ponti, Giovanni (Gio Ponti) 22

Pyramids 8, 9, 42
– Castillo Pyramid, Chicken Itzà 9
– Great Pyramid of Khufu, Giza 9
– Step Pyramid of Djoser, Saqqara 9

Queen Mary (ocean liner) 25

Robert, Alain 27
Rockefeller Jr, John D. 15
Root, John Wellborn 11
Russia
– Moscow 36

San Andreas fault 34
Saudi Arabia 19, 29, 35
– Jeddah 35
– Mecca 29
– Riyadh 19
Sears, Roebuck and Company 27
Seidler, Harry 44
September 11, 2001 7, 25, 36, 37, 45
Shui-bian, president Chen 43
Skyscrapers, towers and buildings
– Al Faisaliah Complex, Riyadh 19
– AT & T Building, New York 30, 31
– Aurora Place, Sydney 39
– Baiyoke II Tower, Bangkok 29
– Bank of America Center, Houston 18, 30
– Bank of China, Hong Kong 28, 43
– Bank of Manhattan Building, New York 12, 16, 17
– Big Ben, London 9
– Burj Al Arab, Dubai 18, 21
– Burj Dubai, Dubai 44
– Canary Wharf Tower, London 20, 30
– CCTV Building, Peking 18, 45
– Central Plaza, Hong Kong 28, 43
– Centro Pirelli, Milan 22
– Chanin Building, New York 15
– Chrysler Building, New York 16–17, 19, 24, 25, 42
– Citicorp Center, New York 21, 35
– CN Tower, Toronto 42
– Commerzbank, Frankfurt 30–31, 35
– Custom House Tower, Boston 13
– EDF Tower, Paris 39
– Eiffel Tower, Paris 9, 16, 19, 38, 39
– Elephant and Castle Eco-Tower, London 44
– Emirates Towers, Dubai 18
– Empire State Building, New York 14–15, 17, 21, 24, 25, 26, 35, 36, 42, 43
– Equitable Building, New York 11, 12
– Flatiron Building, New York 13, 18, 19, 25
– Freedom Tower, New York 25, 35, 36, 37, 42, 43

– Gasometer B Tower, Vienna 18
– GE Building (RCA Building), New York 15
– Giralda Tower, Seville 15
– Grollo Tower, Melbourne 44
– Guaranty Building, Buffalo 11
– Heron Tower, London 39
– Home Insurance Building, Chicago 10
– Hong Kong & Shanghai Bank, Hong Kong 28, 32–33
– IDX Tower, Seattle 39
– Jin Mao Tower, Shanghai 29, 43
– John Hancock Center, Chicago 20, 26, 27
– Kingdom Centre, Riyadh 19
– Lake Point Tower, Chicago 22
– Landmark Tower, Tokyo 29
– Leaning Tower of Pisa, Pisa 8, 9
– Lee Theatre Plaza, Hong Kong 21
– Lever House, New York 23
– Lipstick Building, New York 19
– London Bridge Tower, London 44
– Main Tower, Frankfurt 21
– Maine-Montparnasse Tower, Paris 26
– Masonic Temple, Chicago 11
– McGraw-Hill Building, New York 15
– Messeturm, Frankfurt 30
– Millennium Tower, London 39
– Millennium Tower, Tokyo 38–39
– Municipal Building, New York 12
– Museum of Modern Art, New York 22
– National Bank of Dubai, Dubai 18
– National Commerce Bank, Jeddah 35
– New York Times Building, New York 10
– Ostankino TV Tower, Moscow 36
– Petronas Towers, Kuala Lumpur 21, 29, 30, 40–41, 43
– Radio City Music Hall, New York 15
– Reliance Building, Chicago 10
– Rialto Towers, Melbourne 30
– Rockefeller Center, New York 15, 25
– St. Paul's Cathedral, London 39
– Scandinavian Tower, Malmo 44
– Seagram Building, New York 23
– Sears Tower, Chicago 21, 26–27, 35, 36, 40, 41, 43
– Shanghai World Financial Centre, Shanghai 19, 43
– Shun Hing Square, Shenzhen 43
– Singer Building, New York 13
– Sky Central Plaza,

Guangzhou 43
– Sony Center, Berlin 39
– Swiss Re Headquarters, London 39
– Sydney Opera House, Sydney 39
– Tabung Haji Building, Kuala Lumpur 29
– Taipei 101, Taipei 29, 40, 42–43
– Taj Mahal, Agra 19
– Torre Agbar, Barcelona 19
– Torre Mayor, Mexico City 34
– Tower of Babel, Babylon 8
– Transamerica Building, San Francisco 34
– Tribune Tower, Chicago 15
– Two International Finance Centre, Hong Kong 29, 43
– United Nations Secretariat Building, New York 23
– US Bank Tower, Los Angeles 34
– Waldorf-Astoria Hotel, New York 21
– Wisma 46, Jakarta 19
– Woolworth Building, New York 12, 13, 16, 24, 42
– World Centre for Vedic Learning, India 45
– World Trade Center, New York 25, 26, 35, 36–37, 44, 45
– Wrigley Building, Chicago 15
– 7 South Dearborn Street, Chicago 45
– 120 Wall Street, New York 18
South Korea 28
Spain 8, 15
– Barcelona 19
– Burgos 8
– Seville 15
Sullivan, Louis 11
Sweden 44
– Malmo 44

Tahal, prince Alwaleed bin 19
Taiwan 28, 40, 43
– Taipei 43
Temples 8, 9, 12, 40
– Temple I, Tikal 9
Terrorist attacks 36, 44
Thailand
– Bangkok 29
Think team 37
Tunisia 8
Twin Towers memorial ('Reflected Absence') 37

United Arab Emirates 18, 44
– Dubai 18, 21, 44
United Nations 23

Van Alen, William 16, 17
Vanderbilt, Cornelius 12

Woolworth, Frank Winfield 12
World War Two 14, 22, 28
Wright, Frank Lloyd 45

Yamasaki, Minoru 36
Yogi, Maharishi Mahesh 45

Ziggurats 8, 9, 18, 19
– Ziggurat of Ur 9, 19